Peter & His Pet Petoskey Stone

A Story and Guide for Finding and Polishing
Michigan's Official State Stone

By Victor B. Eichler

Shantimira Press
Three Rivers, Michigan

Peter & His Pet Petoskey Stone, Revised Edition
Copyright © 2014 by Victor B. Eichler

For Jakob, Kody, Kaitlin, Lauren, Katy, Elyse
and grandchildren everywhere.

ISBN: 978-0-9703620-7-0

Shantimira Press
P.O. Box 171
Three Rivers, MI 49093-0171
FAX: 269-244-9047
shantimirapress@yahoo.com

See page 24 for information about ordering more copies of this book, as
well as Petoskey Stone Polishing kits with everything needed—including a
Petoskey Stone—to polish according to the instructions in this book.

Book cover designed by Julie Taylor.

Manufactured in the United States of America

"I found one! I found one!" yelled Peter to his family, who were walking along the shore of Little Traverse Bay, a small part of Lake Michigan. "And it is the most beautiful one in the world!"

Peter's sister and parents came running over to see what Peter had found.

"Look," shouted Peter. "You can see where the little holes used to be! This is a good one for sure!"

What Peter had found was a special stone that is often searched for by people who walk the beaches near the town of Petoskey in Northern Michigan. When dry these stones look dull and gray, but when wet the true nature of them may be seen.

The coral appearance may be faint or absent on the Petoskey Stones when dry.

When wet, the Petoskey Stones show their attractive pattern.

"That's wonderful," said Peter's dad. "Let's take this one home, and I'll show you how to polish it so that its beautiful structure can be seen more clearly. Then it will be a wonderful memory of this vacation together."

Peter's Petoskey stone was as big as the palm of his hand, and it already felt so smooth as he curled his fingers around it. He knew that stones that are in the water a long time get smooth from the movement of the waves that roll them in the water and on the beach.

"But what really is a Petoskey stone," Peter wondered, "and why is it so much more special than any old gray rock?"

His dad began to explain that the Petoskey stone is really a very, very ancient colony of animals, called corals, that used to live in this area when a warm ocean covered most of the state of Michigan. "So, since it once was made up of living animals, what you are holding can be called a fossil," said his father.

Living colonial coral feeding: Each animal (polyp) has a ring of tentacles surrounding the mouth.

Living coral polyps with tentacles withdrawn.

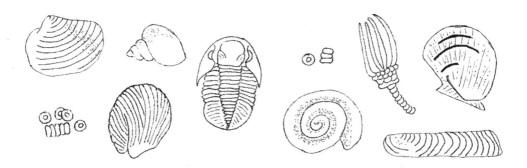

Other fossils which may be found from the same time period.

Over many hundreds of millions of years, the group of skeletons of the once-living coral animals turned hard as stone, which is how a fossil is formed.

Each of the little animals in the group that made up this stone had a mouth where food came in, and that is what looks like the hole in the middle of each cluster in the stone. The little lines that go out from the center once were little parts that helped the coral animal move food from the water into its little mouth opening.

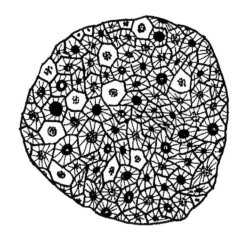

"But now," his dad continued, "the mud that filled in the soft parts has turned to stone, and it has made a very beautiful souvenir for you, Peter."

"Let's go home and polish it," said his dad.

This is what Peter's dad got together to do the polishing:

   220 grit emery paper (fine abrasive wet/dry sandpaper)*
   400 grit emery paper (fine abrasive wet/dry sandpaper)
   600 grit emery paper (fine abrasive wet/dry sandpaper)
   polishing compound (tin oxide or cerium oxide powder)**
   a soft cloth, such as corduroy or cotton towel
   a container of water

Watch what Peter's dad shows Peter, so if you are lucky to find a Petoskey stone someday, you will know how to make it as beautiful as it can be.

---

*   Keeping the sheet wet increases flexibility and improves the finish. The 220 grit is often sold as 'fine,' 400 grit as 'extra fine,' and 600 grit as 'super or ultra fine.'

**   These powders may be ordered online from a rock shop or a lapidary supply house.

Because this special stone had been found on a beach, it had been scratched by other stones as it rolled around in the sand. The tiny pieces of sand on a beach are very hard, but the scratches on Peter's stone are not deep and most can be sanded off with the 220 grit emery paper. This is a type of sandpaper that works well when wet, so Peter and his dad wet the stone and began to rub it all over to make it smoother on the surface.

But the 220 grit paper itself will leave some tiny scratches, so next Peter's dad tells his son to use the 400 grit paper to rub all over the stone. This has tinier bits of material so it will take out finer scratches on the stone.

And finally, Peter's dad wants Peter to rub the whole stone, while wet, with the finest emery paper, which has a number 600 grit. This will leave the surface of the stone very smooth and free of all scratches.

"It looks even more beautiful now," Peter remarked.

"Yes," said his father, "and now it is time to polish it to make it the most beautiful that it can be!"

The stone is best polished with a purchased polishing compound.* However, some products sold for polishing the finish of automobiles can also be used. Peter's dad helps his son mix the polishing compound, and Peter begins to polish the smooth stone with the soft cloth.

"WOW!" Peter shouts out. "Just a little polish makes my Petoskey stone so beautiful and shiny!

"Rub it in well, Peter," his dad says. "And keep polishing, so that the stone really shines."

---

*   Mix the tin oxide or cerium oxide powder with water to the consistency of toothpaste, and rub it on the sanded stone with a moist piece of corduroy or a soft towel.

"You've done an excellent job on cleaning and polishing your stone," said his mother, who had come into the garage to see how Peter and his dad were coming along with their work.

"This is my pet Petoskey stone," Peter happily said as he lifted it up for his mother to see. "I want to take it to school for my teacher to see!"

Peter's teacher was very impressed as Peter told his classmates how he had found his pet stone, and how his dad and he had sanded and polished it to be so beautiful.

Peter was able to tell his teacher that the stone was a fossil of ancient coral animals that once were alive, and that they hardened together over a long, long time in the warm sea.

"Did you know that this is the state stone of Michigan?" his teacher asked. "In 1965, the governor of Michigan made this the official state stone of our state, so you have a genuine stone that represents the state of Michigan!"

"Yes," Peter answered proudly. "And it is my very own pet Petoskey stone!"

SUPPLEMENTARY INFORMATION

including

"Notes On the Natural History of Petoskey Stones"

&

"Where & When to Find Petoskey Stones"

"Notes On the Natural History of Petoskey Stones"

The beautiful rocks known as Petoskey Stones are actually the fossilized skeletons of once-living coral animals that lived in the vast ocean that once covered much of the central United States.

The time when these stones formed is frequently given as the era known as the Middle Devonian, occurring approximately 350 million years before the present time. The rock outcropping of sedimentary rock that formed at that time is known as the Alpena Limestone formation.

This rock formation predominantly reaches the surface near the Michigan city of Petoskey and the nearby Little Traverse Bay area, hence that is why these stones are most common in this area.

STATE OF MICHIGAN

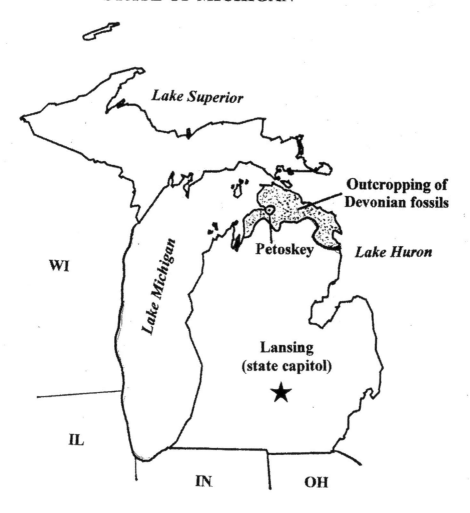

The warm, shallow waters that covered the land which has become the state of Michigan was filled with small invertebrate animals and marine plants. As the ocean waters receded, minerals were deposited in spaces in the remaining skeletal structure of the corals, and they hardened forming the hard stone like the one Peter found in our story.

While glaciers later moved and reformed much of the land in the area, these special fossilized coral remnants were rounded and smoothed before they were finally deposited. Hence, they are quite limited in distribution, usually found only in Michigan's lower peninsula, along beaches of Lake Michigan and inland gravel pits.

There are numerous species of fossilized coral, but the one which has been described as the Petoskey Stone has been given the specific scientific name *Hexagonaria pericarnata*. The name indicates that the individual coral animals had six sides, much like a honeycomb. Such a shape allowed the colonial animals to fit together with little loss of space.

It is easy to walk by the beautiful fossilized stones when they are dry, for the unique pattern shows up best when wet. Many Petoskey Stone seekers will wait for a spring or summer rain to aid them, for when the stones are damp there is a better chance of recognizing them.

On June 28, 1965, Michigan's Governor George Romney signed a bill that made the Petoskey Stone the official state stone. Michigan—and the Petoskey Stone—thus became the first state to recognize a fossil as an Official State Stone!

"Where & When to Find Petoskey Stones"

Two things that need to be considered to successfully find Petoskey stones are WHERE to look and WHEN to look for them!

All along the coast of Little Traverse Bay, which extends about 20 miles west of Petoskey toward Charlevoix along US Highway 31. and the same distance to the north and then west of Petoskey along State Highway 119 past Harbor Springs, are good hunting grounds for the Michigan state rock. When you find public access to the shore it is legal in Michigan to walk along the water's edge to the high water mark without fear of trespassing on private property.

The most consistently good public places to find the Michigan state stone are along the Little Traverse Bay shoreline; the following city and state parks are particularly recommended:

• **Petoskey's Bayfront Park,** site of the Little Traverse History Museum, occasional summer concerts and a paved trail for non-motorized travel that presents spectacular views of Little Traverse Bay. This is also a popular place for finding the fossilized coral stones, so hunting early in the morning before others walk the shoreline is suggested.

• **Magnus City Park and Campground** (summer phone: 231-347-1027), on Little Traverse Bay in Petoskey, has rustic campsites for tents, limited (electric) and full service (water, sewer, electric) campsites and showers during the summer season between April 22 and October 28. It is known as an excellent place to find Petoskey Stones.

• **Fisherman's Island State Park** (231-547-6641), just south of Charlevoix, has five miles of sandy Lake Michigan beach and three miles of hiking trails, plus picnic areas and rustic campgrounds on 2,678 acres of unspoiled land. Petoskey stones are often found on the beach of this beautiful state park.

• **Petoskey State Park** (phone 231-347-2311), located on 304 acres at the north end of Little Traverse Bay, is one and one-half miles north of the city on State Road 119. This park has two separate modern campgrounds with a total of 160 campsites. There is a full mile of sandy beach, and Petoskey Stones are frequently found, especially at the south end of the beach.

• **Leelanau State Park** (phone 231-386-5422) is a 1,350 acre park located on County Road 629, north of the village of Northport, at the tip of the Leelanau Peninsula. The Grand Traverse Lighthouse Museum and more than 8 miles of hiking trails through woods, wetland and over sand dunes are attractions for visitors, along with a rather rocky shoreline where Petoskey stones are frequently found.

• Northport residents also boast of the magnificent sunsets viewed from **Peterson Park,** located on the bluffs overlooking Lake Michigan in Leelanau Township, 26 miles north of Traverse City on State Road 22. The beach below, strewn with rocks, is an excellent place for collecting Petoskey Stones.

In addition to finding Petoskey Stones along the Lake Michigan shore, numerous rock quarries and gravel pits exist where these fossil remains can be found. However, since most of these are on private land, the ambitious rock hunter will need to make his own inquiries in the area.

Because the beautiful pattern of Petoskey Stones is usually not very obvious when the stones are dry, if you are looking in a gravel pit or other place away from the shore, it is best to search for them after a rain while they are still damp. On a beach, look in the shallow water or at the water's edge where they become moistened by the action of the waves.

About the Author & Illustrator

Vic Eichler is a retired college professor who has had a love of all things of the natural world since he was a young boy. Once he moved to Michigan and discovered Petoskey Stones, they provided a natural union of his interests in the biological sciences, marine life, minerals and geologic history. This is his third published book for children (and their parents). He lives with his wife near Three Rivers, Michigan.

Peg Connelly is a self-taught artist who lives in Constantine, Michigan. She is equally comfortable painting with pastels, acrylics, or watercolors as drawing with pen & ink. Peg contributed the illustrations of Peter and his family, the workbench and the scene in the classroom. This is the first published book utilizing her enormous talent! When not creating art, Peg might be seen with any of her nine grandchildren.

Other books available from Shantimira Press
by Victor B. Eichler

"The Awakening of Freddy Tadpole"
A Story for Seekers of All Ages
48 pages · ISBN 978-0-9703620-1-8 · 2001 · $14.95

"Morel Mushrooms in Michigan and Other Great Lakes States"
40 pages · ISBN 978-0-9703620-5-6 · 2010 · $11.95

"Charlevoix Stones & Other Beachcomber Treasures of Northern Michigan"
28 pages · ISBN 978-0-9703620-6-3 · Full Color · 2012 · $9.95

"Passenger Pigeons: Gone Forever!"
Lessons From the Past for the Present and Future
32 pages · ISBN: 978-0-9703620-8-7 · 2014 · $9.95

Also Available:
Petoskey Stone Polishing Kit — or — Charlevoix Stone Polishing Kit
Includes all materials described in this book needed for polishing
(including a Petoskey Stone or Charlevoix Stone), $15 per kit.

Books and Kits are available by mail
Add $3.00 postage & handling for the first item to each address.
Add $2.00 for each additional book or kit sent at the same time.
Michigan residents, add 6% sales tax.

Please contact us for quantity discounts

Shantimira Press
P.O. Box 171
Three Rivers, MI 49093-0171
FAX: 269-244-9047
shantimirapress@yahoo.com

Find us on Facebook:
www.facebook.com/shantimirapress

41243636R00015

Made in the USA
Middletown, DE
04 April 2019